Romance

# Romance

TIM PILCHER

ILEX

● LITTLE BOOK OF VINTAGE: ROMANCE

First published in the UK, US, and Canada
in 2012 by
I L E X
210 High Street
Lewes
East Sussex BN7 2NS
www.ilex-press.com

Copyright © 2012 The Ilex Press Limited

Publisher: Alastair Campbell
Creative Director: Peter Bridgewater
Managing Editor: Nick Jones
Senior Editor: Ellie Wilson
Commissioning Editor: Tim Pilcher
Art Director: Julie Weir
Designer: Simon Goggin

British Library Cataloguing-in-Publication Data
A catalogue record for this book is available
from the British Library.

ISBN: 978-1-908150-41-7

Printed and bound in China

Colour Origination by Ivy Press Reprographics

10 9 8 7 6 5 4 3 2

# Contents

# Introduction

Welcome to the wonderful world of Fifties romance comics! A world of love and marriage, but also of heartache and unrequited passions. A world where everyone searches for their "one, true love" while kissing a lot of frogs along the way.

The first American romance comic, *Young Romance*, was launched in September 1947 and was written and drawn by Joe Simon and Jack Kirby (the creators of *Captain America*). That title spawned an entire genre that flourished for three decades. While they were published right up to 1977, the Golden Age of romance comics was the 1950s. At their peak there were at least 148 different titles on the racks, every month! Every conceivable type of romantic scenario was covered in titles like *G.I. Sweethearts*, *Love Secrets*, and teenage dating in *High School Romance*, to *Cinderella Love*, *My Romantic Adventures*, and even frontier dalliances in *Cowboy Love*. Sales were phenomenal, with top titles selling over 1,000,000 copies each month.

While these "Stirring Tales of Real Romance" were aimed at the target audience of women over 20 years old, they were in fact written and drawn mostly by men such as Frank Frazetta, Wally Wood, John Romita Snr, and Alex Toth—giants in their field. As a result, many of the tales—by today's standards—have sexist endings, with the female characters purely on the hunt for a man to marry—the ultimate dream come true for these lovesick "frails." Titles like *Wedding Bells*, *Just Married*, *Secrets of Young Brides*, *Brides in Love*, and *Brides Romances* helped perpetuate this romantic ideal.

The perfect man could be found just about everywhere, but were ideally surgeons, actors, lawyers, airline pilots, or even better, the boss! And this led to endless tales of nurses, aspiring actresses, stewardesses, and secretaries wistfully thinking, "If only you knew, Earl . . . If you only knew how much I love you! I'll always love you!!" But "the course of true love never did run smooth" and there were plenty of "love rats," "moochers," and "wolves" for these plucky heroines to avoid. And, of course, there were always inscrutable "man-hungry" vamps and no-good dames ready to steal your loved one from under you, if you weren't attentive enough to his needs. But ultimately there was always a happy ending waiting just over the horizon, usually with the steady, dependable guy who'd been overlooked all along.

Inside this fascinating collection of classic comics clips you'll find make-up tips, real life "Dear Doris..." letters, *Date Tips*, quirky ads, full-page splashes, kitsch covers, and complete strips such as *Moochers Never Marry* and *Don't Be Too Feminine!* So snuggle up with your beloved beau and wallow in some shamelessly romantic nostalgia, because "Love's wondrous moments are told here on these pages!"

# Mr. Anthony's
# MAIL BAG

If you have a problem that threatens your happiness, Mr. Anthony can help you. Write to him at his office at the Marital Relations Institute, 15 East 58th Street, New York 22, N.Y.—and space permitting, we'll print your letter and its reply in the "Mail Bag" on these pages. The man who is America's foremost counsellor on human relations can be your personal advisor, just by writing to him.

## ILL... FROM LOVE

Los Angeles, California

Dear Mr. Anthony:

I was going with a young man for seven months and was deeply in love with him. He never said he loved me, and never promised to marry me, but he *did* tell me that he was extremely fond of me and that I made him very happy. We got along very well, never had any disagreement. He liked my family and they liked him, but he never would accept an invitation to dinner at my home, nor would he go to parties that I planned. A few months ago, he suddenly stopped calling. After a few weeks, I wrote and asked for an explanation. He replied that it was not personal, but gave me no reason. Since then I've been quite ill because of this. I've been to the doctors and they tell me to try and get my mind off the subject. I can't sleep, don't eat well, and have lost weight. What shall I do? Shall I try to get him back? I'm very unhappy and need help! N.R.

Dear N.R.—You have my deepest sympathies. There is no pain deeper or greater to the human heart than to love, and not be loved, in return. Alas! It is something that almost everyone experiences at one time or another. The solution to your problem lies in new friends and new interests. Go out socially, your church, your club, dances, beaches... all can help you in the search for a new friend. You must do this for the sake of your health and your peace of mind. The man you love so much, unfortunately does NOT love you. He has shown it in many ways. He would not go to your home, he stopped seeing you, and gave you no plausible reason. Here is good advice for you, N. R. FORGET him, as fast as you can. And do this by making NEW friends immediately!

GOOD-TIME GIRL!
OHHHH!!
LISTEN, BABY-- ULP! POLICE!!
ALL RIGHT, EVERYBODY-- JUST QUIET DOWN...
THERE WAS A TIME WHEN I COULD HOLD MY HEAD UP ANYWHERE... A TIME WHEN MY TORTURED HEART DID NOT KNOW THE ANGUISH AND TORMENT OF GUILT!! BUT THEN THERE CAME ANOTHER TIME-- A TIME WHEN I DISCOVERED ALL THE DESPAIR AND HEARTBREAK OF SHAME!!

# THE ANSWER WOMAN

For every question there is an answer. So, send us your questions, on any subject, and the Answer Woman will answer them for you. ADDRESS ALL QUESTIONS TO:
**THE ANSWER WOMAN, ROOM 603, 241 Church St., N.Y. 13, N. Y.**

Ques: I gave my boy friend a tie for Easter. He wears it when he takes me out. But when he is not with me, he never wears it. I've questioned many of our friends about this. I can't understand why.

*Ans: For heaven's sake, you gave him a tie, not a ball and chain. And I suggest if you like the young man, to stop questioning his friends.*

Girls, don't make my error by mistaking common friendliness for a budding romance!

END

# ASK JANE JONES

Dear Jane,

I have been going with a married man for about two months. He wants to divorce his wife, and marry me. But they have a little boy about a year old.

What should I do? I am 16.

H. J., Chattanooga, Tenn.

In your heart, you already know the answer! Your whole life lies ahead of you. Don't ruin it by committing such a great moral wrong! For your own sake, and for the sake of the innocent child involved, break off with this man immediately!

## TWO BOYS

Dear Peggy:

I have a problem on which I would like your help. There are two boys who like me very much. I like them too. I don't want to break up with them because whenever I see one boy, I forget about the other. This happens when I see one of them. I just seem to forget about the other.

I guess you can say I am two-timing one of them when I go out with the other on a date.

I am 15 years old and I am not allowed to date. When I have fun, I usually do it without my parents knowing it. What do you think I should do?

*G.F., Fredericksburg, Va.*

There is an age-old adage in life, G.F., that says, "You can't have your cake and eat it, too!" And it certainly applies to you. By cheatin on these boys and deceiving your parents the way you are doing, you are setting yourself up in for a tragically severe case of emotional indigestion! Eventually it—or they—will catch up with you, and you will be left with nothing but the hurt. There is a penalty for two-timing . . .

and for sneak-dating. It is very likely to bounce back right into your face . . . and heart. Be honest with these boys, with your parents, and with yourself!

●

## HOW CAN I TELL HIM I LOVE HIM?

Dear Peggy:

I am 18 years old and am in love with a boy who is also 18. I only see him once a week and that is on Saturday night. How can I tell him I love him? I only go out with him once a week and that is just to a show. He takes me home right after the show. Please tell me how I can tell him I love him.

"A Lover."

*You are not supposed to tell him you love him—that is, not until he first declares his love for you and makes known his intentions. Those things are simply not done in nice circles. Carrying your heart on your sleeve is considered cheapening. It is regarded as a reflection—and not a favorable one, at that—on the character of a girl if she takes the initiative in displaying her affections for a boy before he expresses his love for her. Don't place yourself in that category. Remain silent until this young man locates your tongue and lets you know how he feels in this matter. It may even be that you are confused. Perhaps you have mistaken a friendly gesture for a sign of love. If this is so, think of how foolish you would be made to appear? Be on the safe side. Just wait until he tells you, before you tell him.*

# Flames of Fury

"YOU WON'T STEAL MY MAN! NOT WITHOUT A FIGHT!"

When the flame of love burns furiously in your heart, the fire of rage is also easily ignited! Ronny Stevens was my man and I wouldn't stand by and let him be stolen from me! Not without a battle! "All's fair in love and war," they say! And this was both.

# REDUCE KEEP SLIM AT HOME
## WITH RELAXING, SOOTHING MASSAGE!

**ELECTRIC SPOT REDUCER**

*FOR GREATEST BENEFIT IN REDUCING by massage use spot REDUCER with or without electricity— Also used as an aid in the relief of pains for which massage is indicated.*

# TAKE OFF UGLY FAT!
## Don't Stay FAT — You Can LOSE
## POUNDS and INCHES SAFELY without risking HEALTH

Take pounds off—keep slim and trim with Spot Reducer! Remarkable new invention which uses one of the most effective reducing methods employed by masseurs and turkish baths—MASSAGE!

With the SPOT REDUCER you can now enjoy the benefits of RELAXING, SOOTHING massage in the privacy of your own home! Simple to use—just plug in, grasp handle and apply over most any part of the body—stomach, hips, chest, neck, thighs, arms, buttocks, etc. The relaxing, soothing massage breaks down FATTY TISSUES, tones the muscles and flesh, and the increased awakened blood circulation carries away waste fat—helps you regain and keep a firmer and more GRACEFUL FIGURE!

### YOUR OWN PRIVATE MASSEUR AT HOME

When you use the Spot Reducer, it's almost like having your own private masseur at home. It's fun reducing this way! It not only helps you reduce and keep slim—but also aids in the relief of those types of aches and pains—and those tired nerves that can be helped by massage! The Spot Reducer is handsomely made of light weight aluminum and rubber and truly a beautiful invention you will be thankful you own. AC 110 volts.

## TRY THE SPOT REDUCER 10 DAYS FREE IN YOUR OWN HOME!

Mail this coupon with only $1 for your Spot Reducer on approval. Pay postman $8.95 plus delivery—or send $9.95 (full price) and we ship postage prepaid. Use it for ten days in your own home. Then if not delighted return Spot Reducer for full purchase price refund. Don't delay! You have nothing to lose—except ugly, embarrassing, undesirable pounds of FAT. MAIL COUPON now!

### ALSO USE IT FOR ACHES AND PAINS

**CAN'T SLEEP:**
...with electric Spot Reducer. See how soothing gentle massage can be. You sleep when massage can be of benefit.

**MUSCULAR ACHES:**
A handy helper for transient relief of discomforts that can be aided by gentle, relaxing massage.

**USED BY EXPERTS:**
Thousands have lost weight this way—in hips, abdomen, legs, arms, necks, buttocks, etc. The same method used by stage, screen and radio personalities and leading reducing salons. The Spot Reducer can be used in your spare time, in the privacy of your own room.

**ORDER IT TODAY!**

# *Two*

ONE IS VE

I TH

BU

I T

BUT O

IT TAKES

*Loves*

SE;

MES HE'S SLIPPING.

E JOY TO HAVE THAT
     BOY

AT MY HEELS A-NIPPING!

THER'S FAR AWAY;

T TIMES HE'S BETTER,

GRIEF AND GREAT
F

E BY LETTER!

# Sneak Thief

"Take that blouse off, Emily Thompson! You know that's the only new thing I've gotten in two months!" I was ready to tear it off my sister's back. Because Emily was two years older, she received all the new clothes and I got them as hand-me-downs. This blouse I had gotten new and now she, who had all the clothes she wanted, had taken that too ... And I knew why! George was coming tonight and George was *my* boyfriend!

"You know you only want to wear it so that George will think it was yours to start with!" I screamed, "but you know that won't empress him, because he loves ME!"

"We'll see about that!" Emily smiled at me in that sly way that fascinated all the boys in our school. I knew she had wanted George for herself for a long time ... ever since I let him take me home the first time. Since then, she had constantly played up to him. She had all the dates she wanted—maybe because she had fancy new clothes. I was determined she would not win this time! George was all mine and he was no school kid. He worked at the bank since his graduation last year.

"You won't be able to hold George—and it won't be because of this stupid blouse either." She tore it off and threw it on my bed. With a sarcastic gesture of the hand, she left the room. I hated her then—even if she was my sister!

I took the blouse from the bed. It w[as] not very wrinkled because Emily had on[ly] worn it a few minutes. Then I put it on[. I] had to look especially pretty. I looked [for] the little locket George had given me [for] my last birthday. It was not in its pla[ce] in the dresser drawer. I searched all ov[er] frantically until the bell rang and I rush[ed] downstairs to meet George. He look[ed] angry. Could Emily have spoken to h[im] on the porch and poisoned his mi[nd] against me?

"Your sister is nothing but a snea[k] thief! Did you know she was wearing t[he] locket I gave you?" George was sizzl[ing] with indignation. But then—at the sig[ht] of my unhappy face he stopped. A sm[ile] spread across his face. "That wasn't [the] *only thing* she tried to steal darling. [At] least when you and I are married y[ou] won't have to worry that you're steali[ng] me from her! I've been yours all along!"

So he knew. He took me in his arm[s] and I knew soon I would be first in h[is] house—I was *first* in his *heart* already.

## FIRST KISS

Mickey and I had come home af[ter] the school dance. We got on the subj[ect] of heartbeats. He took my hand to f[eel] my pulse. "My, but your pulse is slow," [he] said. "Mind if I speed it up a bit?" I d[idn't] know what he meant so I said: "Sure, [go] ahead!" He pulled me over to him a[nd] kissed me. Well my pulse *did* beat mu[ch] much faster after that! I knew Mickey [had] tricked me, but it was wonderful!

*T.L., Sacramento, Cali.*

I TRIED TO MAKE MYSELF ATTRACTIVE... THERE WASN'T A COSMETIC I DIDN'T OWN...LIPSTICK, POWDER, ROUGE...THE WORKS. BUT MERELY OWNING THEM WASN'T ENOUGH, I DIDN'T KNOW...

I'LL BET JANE WOULDN'T BE A BAD LOOKER WITHOUT THAT MASK ON.

I TH... MAKE... SUPPO... FLA... A G...

# HOW TO USE MAKE-UP

A LOVE LESSON BEAUTY FEATURE

"NEXT CAME THE ROUGE..."
I THOUGHT YOU PUT ROUGE ON AFTER THE POWDER.
WELL, POWDER ROUGE DOES. GO ON AFTER THE POWDER, BUT CREAM ROUGE SHOULD BE APPLIED BEFORE IT. JUST PUT THREE DOTS ON EACH CHEEK AND THEN BLEND... ALWAYS UPWARD!

## "THE POWDER FOLLOWED..."

TO BEGIN WITH, PUT A LOT OF POWDER ON YOUR PUFF AND DAB IT FREELY ALL OVER YOUR FACE, WITHOUT RUBBING. BUT MOST OF ALL YOU WANT TO AVOID THAT POWDERY LOOK, SO WITH A PIECE OF COTTON DAB YOUR SKIN LIGHTLY UNTIL YOU'VE REMOVED EVERY GRAIN OF EXCESS POWDER.

GEE, MY SKIN LOOKS SO CLEAR AND NATURAL!

"FOUNDATION, POWDER AND ROUGE ALL IN PLACE, I WAS READY FOR THE LIPSTICK. WITH A SMALL LIPSTICK BRUSH, MISS FROST FOLLOWED THE OUTLINE OF MY LIPS AND..."
THERE, JANE. I THINK THAT ABOUT DOES IT. GO VERY EASY ON THE LIPSTICK AND USE A SOFT SHADE...WELL HOW DO YOU LIKE YOURSELF?
HONESTLY, MISS FROST, I FEEL LIKE A NEW WOMAN. I CAN'T WAIT TILL EVERYONE SEES ME.

# SMALL BRA WOMEN

## HEART THROBS
# *Advice on Love Problems*

Dear Marilyn Minton:

My buddy and I both like the same girl, but we're such good friends, we never even get to date her alone. When I take her out, he tags along and when he sees her, I'm there. It's starting to annoy me and I guess he gets mad, too. Shall I ask our girl to choose between us? I would certainly like to get this thing settled.

Very truly Yours, Ned C. Allentown, Pa.

Dear Ned:

Have a serious talk with your friend and try to agree to see this girl without the other one present. In this way you won't force her to make a difficult decision and you can keep your friendship with the other boy.

Marilyn Minton

♥ ♥ ♥

BITTER WORDS! ACCUSATIONS! VIOLENT QUARRELS THAT LEFT ME CONFUSED AND SHAKEN! I COULDN'T REMEMBER A TIME WHEN MY PARENTS WEREN'T FIGHTING, OR MISERABLY RECOVERING FROM THEIR LAST HYSTERICAL OUTBREAK! NO WONDER I LEARNED TO ASSOCIATE MARRIAGE WITH ANGER, HEARTRENDING EMOTIONS AND TEARS! NO WONDER THAT I VOWED NEVER TO PLUNGE MYSELF INTO THE SAME SEA OF DESPAIR THAT I HAD COWERED BEFORE SINCE CHILDHOOD! EVEN WHEN MY HEART CRIED OUT FOR ROMANCE MY LIPS SOUNDED A WARNING TO THE MAN I LOVED...

# DON'T MENTION MARRIAGE TO ME

FIGHT, FIGHT, FIGHT! THAT'S ALL YOU KNOW! YOU CAN'T EVEN SHUT UP IN FRONT OF SUSAN'S BOYFRIEND!

MAYBE SHE'LL WAKE UP AND SEE WHAT MARRIAGE MEANS! YOU MADE A SHAMBLES OF MY LIFE AND I DON'T WANT THIS TO HAPPEN TO HER!

# SOMETHING NEW...
## Something DIFFERENT!

OR THE FIRST
ME...THRILL-LADEN
OMANCES...GRIPPING
VE STORIES! HEART-
ROB TALES YOU'LL
MEMBER FOREVER...
CAUSE THEY MIGHT
VE-HAPPENED TO
OU! FOR GREAT
DVENTURES IN
MANCE...FOR THE
OST CAPTIVATING
VE STORIES EVER
LD...

## Don't Miss

U'VE HEARD THE EXPRESSION: "POOR LITTLE RICH GIRL"...THAT'S ME! MY FATHER
S THE RICHEST MAN IN NEWPORT...WHICH RAISED ONE SERIOUS QUESTION IN MY
ND: WHEN A BOY PROPOSED, WAS IT ME HE WANTED...OR THE FORTUNE THAT CAME
WITH ME?

# WANTING YOU

YOU MEAN SO MUCH TO ME, PAMELA! I WANT YOU FOR MY WIFE!

DO LIKE YOU, US...BUT I'M SURE IT'S LOVE!

YOU'LL LEARN TO CARE, DARLING...IN TIME!

I'M SORRY, DOUG...IT'S NOT ENOUGH TO BASE A MARRIAGE ON! WE'D BETTER JOIN THE OTHERS IN THIS HOUSE NOW!

1

# On the threshold of love's awakening

*...the vows made*
*...the words whispered*
*...the hopes envisioned*

ALL REVEALED IN THE PICTURE ROMANCE STORIES OF

## ROMANTIC SECRETS

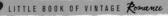 

# DATE TIPS

🎀 🎀 🎀

## *"How to Get That Second Date"*

You've finally had a date with your dream man, and now you're sitting near the phone waiting for him to call. Only silence greets you and you question yourself, "What did I do wrong? Why doesn't he like me?"

There may be many reasons, but the biggest reason may be that he didn't feel comfortable with you. There were long stretches of silence and the whole evening bogged down into a flat soggy pancake.

Now the next time you get a first date and really want another, here are a few tips for you. Be sweet from the moment he enters your home. Let him talk to your parents and add to the conversation. Don't argue with Mother, Dad, or the kids. Your boy friend will like you better if you don't. Remember, he has a family too.

To keep the evening lively and to keep your boy friend happy and comfortable, it's up to you to get the conversation started. The best way is to start with a question. When you're alone, tell him when you noticed him first. If possible remark about what he was wearing at the time. This will flatter him. Your follow-up is, "When was the first time you noticed me?" Now he'll talk and before long you'll be reminiscing happily.

When that topic is exhausted, speak about some mutual friend. Never be a gossip, just question what he thinks about different people. Another good starter is the movies. Ask him who his favorite star is and what pictures he's seen lately. This last can go on for a long time, if you're both interested in the movies.

Dogs are a wonderful topic—or any pets for that matter. Ask him about his pets, then discuss feeding, cute tricks they do, etc.

If your boy friend is the serious type, open a conversation with some news item that has appeared lately. (You might look one up before he comes.) This will open a wonderful avenue of talk. You won't have to be brilliant. Just listen to him.

As a last warning, never open a conversation with a question that requires only a "yes" or a "no." It will be over before you start.

If you readers have any date tips, send them to me. I'll be glad to publish them.—Diane Mason

"I understood all too clearly! I understood that this was my last chance ... and I wouldn't give up... until...
OK, BABY! IF YOU'RE CRAZY ENOUGH...MAYBE I CAN USE A NURSEMAID AFTER ALL! COME HERE!

AND HE NEVER WILL MENTION THOSE TOPICS -- BECAUSE MOOCHERS ARE TIGHTWADS WITH LOVE AS WELL AS MONEY! SO YOU'D BETTER WASH THAT PARASITE OUT OF YOUR HAIR -- BEFORE HE TAKES YOU FOR ALL YOU'VE GOT!

# *Mr. Anthony's*
# MAIL BAG

If you have a problem that threatens your happiness, Mr. Anthony can help you. Write to him at his office at the Marital Relations Institute, 15 East 58th Street, New York 22, N.Y.—and space permitting, we'll print your letter and its reply in the "Mail Bag" on these pages. The man who is America's foremost counsellor on human relations can be your personal advisor, just by writing to him.

## THE PROBLEM OF THE DRINKER

Mattapan, Massachusetts

Dear Mr. Anthony:

I have been going with a boy now for over a year. He is 22 and I am 18. We love each other dearly. He is very fine in many ways, thoughtful and good. He has a rather poorly paying job, but I work, also. My parents are comfortably well off, but here is my problem. Every month or so, he goes on a "binge," and remains drunk for two or three days. Then he sobers up and is his dear self again. When he is drunk, he is very abusive, and my parents have threatened to have him arrested if he comes around again. But I love him more than life itself, and can't give him up.

I have even let him have some of my savings, as he spends all his money when he goes out on his drinking bouts. I am at my wit's end to know what to do. Shall I give him up, as my parents say? Or shall I marry him, and try to reform him? Maybe a home and family and responsibility will change him? K.A.

Dear K.A.—Marriage is not a reformatory. It has never been done and never will. But you might advise your boy friend to see a psychiatrist. Perhaps he is ill, has some deep and painful problem. He needs help. Then there is the famous A.A. (Alcoholics Anyonymous). They might help him. But whatever you do... DON'T MARRY HIM, until he is completely cured. And also... you are so young... Wait, look around, and perhaps you will find someone more worthy of your love and devotion. Good luck to you!

# "MY BRIEF ENCOUNTER."

I WAS ON THE TRAIN HEADED THE EAST COAST... I WAS TO MEET JULIUS, MY FIANCE ...HE WAS GOING TO BE MUSTERED OUT OF THE SERVICE THE FOLLOWING DAY. EVERYTHING WAS GOING SMOOTHLY, I COULD HARDLY WAIT TO SEE JULIUS AGAIN ...BUT A VERY STRANGE THING HAPPENED TO ME... A BRIEF ENCOUNTER ON THE TRAIN WHEN I MET THE *HANDSOME BLONDE STRANGER* WITH THE BLACK PATCH OVER HIS EYE...

WINIK OSRIN

I KNOW WE'VE ONLY BEEN ON THIS TRAIN FOR A LITTLE OVER A DAY, SYLVIA ...AND I FIND MYSELF FALLING FOR YOU HEAD OVER HEELS ... PLEASE ...PLEASE DON'T THINK ME TOO BOLD... I JUST CAN'T RESIST YOU!

WHAT'S COME OVER ME? I'M REACTING TO HIS WILL AS IF I WERE HYPNOTIZED!

LIKE PUTTY IN HIS ARMS I SEEMED TO MELT INTO WHATEVER WHIM THIS MYSTERIOUS STRANGER HAD IN M... WAS IT LOVE ...TORRID AND SUDDEN ?... NO, IT COULD BE ...I WAS NOT THAT TYPE OF GIRL ...THEN WHAT WA... IT ? WHY WAS I KISSING THIS *LOVE PIRATE*... THIS BITTER *STRANGER*...

# HE TRIED TO POSSESS ME

THE man I loved wanted to own me body and soul. Jealousy and smug ownership kept me a prisoner. My foolish snobbery and false sense of values almost lost me real love and real happiness.

"YOU'LL DO AS I SAY, MARIANNE! THERE WILL BE NO ONE ELSE IN YOUR LIFE BUT ME. DO YOU HEAR? YOU'RE MINE AND MINE ONLY!"

"NO, OH NO DONALD!"

IT all began when my parents were killed in an auto accident, leaving me, Marianne Court, an orphan at nineteen...

"WHAT WILL I EVER DO?"

"I'M SO SORRY, MAY I DRIVE YOU HOME? I'M MR. SIMON."

"IT'S A GREAT LOSS...IF I CAN BE OF ANY HELP, CALL ON ME...I'M MR. SIMON OF SIMON'S DEPARTMENT STORE."

"NO, I'LL STAY HERE. BUT THANK YOU. I'LL REMEMBER, MR. SIMON."

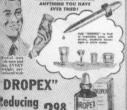

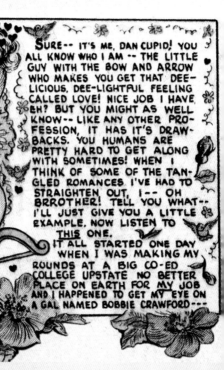

SURE-- IT'S ME, DAN CUPID! YOU ALL KNOW WHO I AM -- THE LITTLE GUY WITH THE BOW AND ARROW WHO MAKES YOU GET THAT DEE-LICIOUS, DEE-LIGHTFUL FEELING CALLED LOVE! NICE JOB I HAVE, EH? BUT YOU MIGHT AS WELL KNOW-- LIKE ANY OTHER PRO-FESSION, IT HAS IT'S DRAW-BACKS. YOU HUMANS ARE PRETTY HARD TO GET ALONG WITH SOMETIMES! WHEN I THINK OF SOME OF THE TAN-GLED ROMANCES I'VE HAD TO STRAIGHTEN OUT, I -- OH BRROTHER! TELL YOU WHAT-- I'LL JUST GIVE YOU A LITTLE EXAMPLE. NOW LISTEN TO THIS ONE.

IT ALL STARTED ONE DAY WHEN I WAS MAKING MY ROUNDS AT A BIG CO-ED COLLEGE UPSTATE NO BETTER PLACE ON EARTH FOR MY JOB AND I HAPPENED TO GET MY EYE ON A GAL NAMED BOBBIE CRAWFORD---

# PIMPLES

## dry up in 3 days
## OR YOUR MONEY BACK!

**At** last science has discovered a fast, harmless way to clear your skin of those horrible pimples, blackheads and acne spots. This is an entirely new, greaseless cream that contains powerful A and D vitamins. It works fast by drying out the superfluous skin oils pimples feed on... at the same time counteracts by antiseptic action, the growth of bacteria that cause and spread ugly skin blemishes.

### IMPROVE YOUR APPEARANCE WITH FIRST APPLICATION

You look better the minute you apply wonder-working CLEAR-X, because its amazing skin color hides the blemishes while its medicinal action gets to work clearing them up fast. You don't risk a penny. Get CLEAR-X by sending in the coupon now, use it for 3 days, and if your skin troubles are not definitely improved, you pay nothing.

## LOVE CAN BE YOURS AGAIN

You can't blame him (or her) for not wanting to [kiss] you if your skin is oily, defaced with ugly pimp[les] blackheads and acne spots. Give yoursel[f a] break! CLEAR-X will clear your skin like ma[gic]

## FREE IF YOU ACT NOW!

A $3.00 jar of CLEAR-X medicated soap to help CLEAR-X work even faster with double action. That's a $6.00 value for just $2.98.

# YOU Can Be a *Prettie*

### by Phyllis Pool, *Beauty Expert*

In each issue of this magazine you will be shown that there is
ugly girl. Because health, cleanliness and naturalness are the
there is no reason, or excuse, to be unattractive.

**Rouge is important.** You should use cream rouge, applying
tion lotion but before your powder. If your face is oval, and
dab two or three small spots of cream rouge just over your c
your hairline on either side of your face. Then, blend these
ing the color from the middle of the cheek out, and up to ju
member to fade the color gradually. By practicing, you
little you need use and how natural it looks with the ed
your own skin color. Notice, too, how it brightens your e

If you think that your face is too round, try this: Apply
of cream rouge near your hairline high up on either side o
the middle of your cheek, and, as you blend it back aga
your jawline. Now, notice how much slimmer your face

Your face may be too long and thin. Apply the dots o
cheekbone and out to the hairline but work them back
very top of your cheek and as far away from your nos
line as possible.

You will find that rouge comes in many shades and
this confuse you, they reduce to basic tones; some w
and some blue-red. Once you have determined whic
9.        ing you can make your selection from the many rou
And, when you're prettier, aren't you happier?

# Darling

...hing as an
...uirements,

...our founda-
...little color,
...and toward
...ther, spread-
...your eyes. Re-
...kly learn how
...ded right into

...three light dots
...it down toward
...it down toward

...starting on your
...the color near the
...close to your hair-

...mes, but don't let
...ge, some clear red
...best for your color-
...g that basic tone.

# DON'T
## be a
# "COMPARE

BUT YOU DON'T KNOW AUGUSTA! SHE CAN'T LET WELL ENOUGH ALONE···YOU SEE, SHE'S A **COMPARER**···

I'VE WORKED HARD, BUT IT'S BEEN WORTH IT! IT GOT ME THE SWELL JOB I HAVE···THE BEST JOB EVER···

OH, IT'S ALL RIGHT··· BUT IT'S NOTHING COMPARED TO THE JOB **TOM JENSEN** HAS! HE'S THIS BOY I KNOW ···HE MAKES MUCH MORE THAN YOU, AND HE'S GOT MUCH MORE OPPORTUNITY FOR ADVANCEMENT THAN YOU HAVE!

# MY BLIND DATE

How did YOUR blind date turn out? Was it a DREAM-DATE or a DRIP-DATE? Did it start you on the road to ROMANCE—or did it reach the END OF THE LANE, by midnight?

Remember, FIRST ROMANCE pays $2,00 for each true story printed in this column!

Write to:   MY BLIND DATE CONTEXT
FIRST ROMANCE
1860 Broadway
New York 23, N. Y.

When my girl-friend, Anita, told me she had a blind date for me, I accepted gladly. She said he was nice, new in town, and didn't know anyone but her and her boy-friend.

So, when the four of us got into the car, I was sure we were going to a movie or a nice night-club. But after an hour of riding, my date, Tony, told me he was broke. So I loaned him five dollars which he promised to return to me the next day. After that, we had lots of fun, and Tony and I made a date for the next night.

All this happened two years ago. I haven't seen Tony since—or my five dollars either!

B.L.R., Amarillo, Texas.

ROMAN[CE]

WORL[D]

IN SOME ISLANDS OF THE PACIFIC, BABIES ARE BETHROTHED AT BIRTH!

# THE OVER

LONG AGO, AMONG THE COMMON PEOPLES OF THE EARTH, IT WAS A CUSTOM TO BREAK A PIECE OF GOLD OR SILVER TO SEAL THE BETHROTHAL PACT. ONE HALF WAS KEPT BY THE WOMAN, THE OTHER HALF BY THE MAN!

# Nobody's DARLING

HAD THE SWEETHEART PARADE PASSED ME BY? WAS I NEVER TO EXPERIENCE THE SUPREME HAPPINESS OF BEING IN THE ARMS OF SOMEONE I LOVED? SUDDENLY I SAW MYSELF AS I WAS, A SAD AND SOLITARY FIGURE, THE GIRL WHO HAD ALWAYS BEEN EVERYBODY'S PAL AND WOULD NEVER BE ANYBODY'S DARLING!

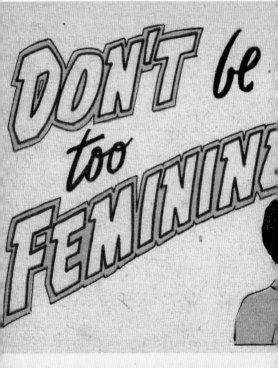

# I Ran Away From Sham

MY CARELESS FLINGS AT ROMANCE WERE THE TALK OF THE TOWN. I LAUGHED AT THE RAISED EYEBROWS AND THE GOSSIP THAT WAS WHISPERED BEHIND MY BACK. I WAS HAVING A WONDERFUL TIME--UNTIL MY ESCAPADES WENT TOO FAR AND CAME TO THE ATTENTION OF MY PARENTS. THEN MY TRUANT CONSCIENCE WAS CAUGHT IN A TANGLE OF SHAME, FRIGHTENED BY THE BITTER CONSEQUENCES, I LOST MY HEAD IN A FRANTIC DESIRE TO ESCAPE. BUT IN MY FLIGHT FROM SHAME, I FELL BACK INTO THE WAYS THAT HAD BEEN MY UNDOING. I NEVER DREAMED THAT TRUE LOVE COULD TAME MY ERRANT EMOTIONS. THE CHANCE CAME AFTER I HAD FALLEN FOR THE WRONG FELLOW. BUT I HAD TO SUFFER A SECOND HEARTBREAK TO EARN MY RIGHT TO LOVE AND BE LOVED.

YOU'RE A DISGRACE TO US, STELLA! WE HAD NO IDEA THAT YOU WERE RUNNING AROUND NIGHTS WITH THE BOYS WHO WORK IN MY GROVES!

BUT, DAD I DIDN'T DO ANYTHING REALLY WRONG. YOU MUS BELIEVE GOSSIP--EVEN IF IT'S PRINTED!

# OW THEY WERE MARRIED!

HELP! ...ES! ...ME ...O!

NO! YOU'RE GOING TO BE MY WIFE!

...PRE-HISTORIC TIMES, CAVEMEN CAPTURED THEIR ...IES! WHETHER THE GIRL WANTED TO MARRY HIM ...OT, NEVER OCCURRED TO THE PRIMITIVE HUSBAND! THE GIRL'S SAKE, WE HOPE IT DIDN'T MATTER!

WHILE IN COMPARATIVELY MODERN TIMES, GIRLS WERE SOLD TO THEIR HUSBANDS! THE PRETTIER THE GIRL, THE MORE HER FATHER COULD ASK!

YOU'LL HAVE TO DO BETTER! JOEL HUGHES HAS OFFERED THREE COWS!

ALL RIGHT! I'LL GIVE YOU FOUR COWS AND ALL THE HAY THEY CAN EAT!

AROUND THE WORLD, INFANT BE-TROTHALS ARE THE WAY SOME FOLKS MARRY! IN THE SOUTH SEAS—

ARE ONE! PAR—...YOU WILL CARE ...THIS COUPLE... THEY ARE ...ENOUGH TO ...CARE FOR ...THEMSELVES!

ORIENTAL MARRIAGES WERE ALWAYS AR-RANGED BY "GO-BETWEENS" HIRED BY THE GIRL'S PARENTS. SHE NEVER SAW HER HUSBAND UNTIL AFTER THE CERE-MONY, WHICH, IN MANY CASES, SHE DID NOT ATTEND!

WE ACCEPT THE YOUNG MAN YOU CHOOSE FOR OUR DAUGHTER!

IT IS GOOD, N'BALI! I AM SATISFIED TO BE YOUR HUSBAND... YOU CAN COOK!

AMONG SOME AFRICAN TRIBES, EATING A MEAL TO-GETHER CONSTITUTES A LEGAL MARRIAGE CEREMONY!

...ILE SEVERAL INDIAN TRIBES OF ...RICA USED THE "MARRIAGE BY ...IDEA. IF A GIRL ACCEPTED A WAR ...NY, A PERSIMMON OR BEADED ...LRY FROM A BRAVE, IT MEANT ...WAS WILLING TO BE KNOWN AS HIS WIFE!

ONLY IN THE TWENTIETH CENTURY, AND MAINLY IN THIS COUNTRY, HAS MARRIAGE SOLELY FOR LOVE BEEN THE MOST COMMON IDEAL!

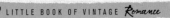